The story of Tenali Raman and the Cat

An imprint of Om Books International

King Krishna Deva Raya was a wise and kind king who ruled over Vijaynagar for many years in peace. He was assisted in his kingly duties by his faithful personal advisor, Tenali Raman.

Tenali was a man of immense wit and intellect, and had a flair for poetry. He was the problem solver in all state matters. The King often came to him for help and assistance.

Once, the kingdom of Vijaynagar faced a problem. The population of rats had come to be a major issue that was hampering everyday life. The number of rats had boomed in a month.

The rats were destroying everything. Documents, books, grains, stores, clothes-nothing was spared, the rats bit through them all.

The population of cats in the kingdom could not cope up with this startlingly large number of rats and were ineffective at pest control. Seeing this, the king issued a notice asking each household to adopt a cat.

Since cats drink milk, and not all homes in the kingdom housed a cow, the king donated a cow to each house to solve this problem. The people were satisfied and took great care of the cats and the cows. The milk from the cow went to the cat who caught the rat, and everyone was happy.

Tenali Raman was very fond of drinking milk. He wished to keep the milk from the cow for himself and not give it to the cat. So he came up with a clever plan to make sure his cat never got any of the milk.

He boiled the milk till it was very hot and poured it onto a dish for the cat. The cat would come running seeing the milk, but as soon as it touched the hot milk, its tongue would get burnt and scalded, and it would run away crying.

Tenali Raman cruelly repeated the same procedure for a period of seven days. At the end of it, the cat stopped trusting Tenali and refused to touch the milk

for fear of getting its tongue burned. In this way, Tenali kept all the milk for himself and let the poor cat starve.

The king asked all the subjects in his kingdom to bring the pet cats before him for inspection. While everyone had been feeding their cat with great care and love, Tenali had been ungrateful to his cat and

caused it much misery and pain. His cat was thin, weak and meowed feverishly. The King was furious, and accused Tenali of torturing the cat by depriving it of food.

"It is not my fault, Your Majesty. My cat does not drink milk," lied Tenali.

"That is not possible!" thundered the King. He ordered milk to be brought before the cat.

As soon as the milk was poured into a dish, the cat ran away scared. The King was astonished, but he understood that Tenali had been torturing the cat as nothing else would have caused it to run away.

As punishment, Tenali had to drink only milk for the next six months and by the end of it, he did not want to touch a drop of milk again, just like the cat.